Supporting Maths

FOR AGES 5–6

Introduction

Supporting Maths is aimed at all those who work with children who have been identified as needing 'additional' or 'different' support in mathematics. It can be used by anyone working with children who fall into this category, whether you are a teacher, classroom assistant or parent.

Typically the five to six year-old children for whom the book is intended will be working at the levels expected of Foundation Stage children or they may simply need extra help in tackling the level of work appropriate for Year 1. Their difficulties may be short term, and overcome with extra practice and support on a one-to-one or small group basis, or they may be long term, where such support enables them to make progress but at a level behind their peer group. The *Record and Review* sheet on page 5 is ideal for keeping track of the targets you set and the progress made by each child.

The 2006 Framework for Teaching Mathematics specifies seven strands of learning:

Strand 1   Using and applying mathematics
Strand 2   Counting and understanding number
Strand 3   Knowing and using number facts
Strand 4   Calculating
Strand 5   Understanding shape
Strand 6   Measuring
Strand 7   Handling data

This book addresses all seven strands, drawing on the Key Stage 1 objectives. Particular emphasis is placed on understanding number, using number facts and calculating with these. The *Individual record sheet* on page 3 shows the aspects of the seven strands that can be assessed through using the worksheets and through discussion with the pupil.

In this book we provide activities that can be effectively completed on paper, with the help of an adult. The interaction with the adult gives many opportunities for speaking and listening. Explanation by an adult to a child and vice versa provides a firm foundation for mathematical understanding. To reinforce understanding, many activities should be completed in a practical context e.g. children could count real items; they could compare sizes of real objects; they could perform practical addition by combining two groups of objects; they could perform subtractions by removing objects from a set and seeing how many remain.

Several worksheets deal with counting. Accurate counting is a **vital** skill and is sometimes neglected. Its importance should not be underestimated as many children fail to develop effective strategies for counting. Once these children are asked to perform calculations such as additions and subtractions their inability to count accurately can result in errors. Thus, although they may be able to cope with the number operation, these counting errors result in incorrect answers and cause the children to lose confidence in their ability to perform the operation itself. Many activities address the key skills of adding and subtracting. Pupils are supported by the pictures of animals, shapes and other objects on the worksheets and by the 'number ladders', which form useful number lines to help in the visualisation of adding and subtracting.

However you decide to use these sheets and in whatever context, it is worth remembering that children generally achieve the greatest success in an atmosphere of support and encouragement. Praise from a caring adult can be the best reward for the children's efforts. The worksheets and activities in this book will provide many opportunities for children to enjoy their successes. (As a visual reminder, children can also complete the *My record sheet* on page 4). The development of a positive attitude and the resulting increase in self-esteem will help them with all of their school work and other areas of school life too.

Individual record sheet

Name:

Worksheet	Contents	Teaching and learning objective	Target achieved	Needs more practice
1-7	How many?	Strands 1, 2		
8	How many shapes?	Strands 1, 2, 5		
9	How many sides?	Strands 1, 2, 5		
10-12	How many do you think?	Strands 1, 2, 5		
13	How many circles and triangles?	Strands 1, 2, 5		
14	How many circles and squares?	Strands 1, 2, 5		
15-17	Write the numbers	Strands 1, 2		
18-20	Draw one more	Strands 1, 2, 3, 4, 5		
21-22	How many altogether?	Strands 1, 2, 4, 5		
23-24	Make ten	Strands 1, 2, 3, 4, 5		
25	Continue the patterns	Strands 1, 2, 4, 5, 7		
26-30	Adding	Strands 1, 2, 3, 4		
31-32	Subtracting	Strands 1, 2, 3, 4		
33-39	Adding using number ladders	Strands 1, 2, 3, 4		
40-45	Subtracting using number ladders	Strands 1, 2, 3, 4		
46	A clock face	Strands 1, 2, 3, 5, 6, 7		
Resource sheets				
A-B	Number cards	Strands 1, 2		
C	Number and word cards	Strands 1, 2		
D	Word cards	Strands 1, 2		
E-G	Counting cards	Strands 1, 2		
H	Dice patterns and shapes	Strands 1, 2, 5		
I-K	Shapes	Strand 5		
L	Clock numbers	Strands 1, 2, 3, 5, 6, 7		
M	Number ladders	Strands 1, 2, 3, 4,		

My record sheet

Name: _____   Date of birth: _____

Class: _____   Date: _____

I can...

- say and use the number names in order ☐

- count up to five objects ☐

- count up to ten objects ☐

- recognise numerals 1 to 9 ☐

- write numerals 1 to 9 ☐

- match sets of objects to appropriate numerals ☐

- estimate numbers of objects and check by counting ☐

- use 'more' or 'less' to compare two numbers ☐

- find one more or one less than a number from 1 to 10 ☐

- begin to relate addition to combining two groups ☐

- use the names 'circle', 'square' and 'triangle' ☐

- use everyday language related to time ☐

- talk about, recognise and recreate simple patterns ☐

- sort familiar objects and count how many share a particular property ☐

Andrew Brodie: Supporting Maths © A & C Black Publishers Ltd. 2007

Record and Review

Name: _____   Date of birth: _____

Teacher: _____   Class: _____

Support assistant: _____

Code of Practice stage: _____   Date targets set: _____

Target

1 _____

2 _____

3 _____

4 _____

Review

Target

1 _____

_____

_____ Target achieved? ☐ Date: _____

2 _____

_____

_____ Target achieved? ☐ Date: _____

3 _____

_____

_____ Target achieved? ☐ Date: _____

4 _____

_____

_____ Target achieved? ☐ Date: _____

Name: _____ **Date:** _____

How many birds?

How many cats?

How many?

Notes for teachers

Target: Match sets of objects to numerals (Strand 1). Say and use number names; count reliably up to 10; match then compare the numbers of objects in two sets; use 'more' or 'less' to compare two numbers; recognise numerals 1 to 9 (Strand 2).

Look at each set with the child and discuss the number of items. Help the child write the correct number in each box. Alternatively the s/he could stick the number cut out from Resource sheet A on the box. If the child is confident, ask her/him whether there are more cats than birds or fewer cats than birds. Then discuss the fact that three is more than two and two is less than three. In the last box the child should draw some items of their own and write the appropriate number to go with them.

Andrew Brodie: Supporting Maths © A & C Black Publishers Ltd. 2007

Name: _____   Date: _____

How many stars?

How many squares?

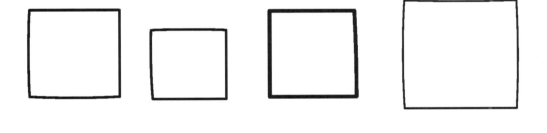

How many?

Notes for teachers
Target: Match sets of objects to numerals (Strand 1). Say and use number names; count reliably up to 10; match then compare the numbers of objects in two sets; use 'more' or 'less' to compare two numbers; recognise numerals (Strand 2). Use language to describe the shape and size of flat shapes (Strand 5).
Look at each set with the child and discuss the number of items. Help the child to find the correct number to stick in the box (cut out from Resource sheet A) or to write the number in the box. If the child is confident, ask him/her whether there are more squares than stars or fewer squares than stars. Then discuss the fact that four is more than one and that one is less than four. This activity also provides the opportunity to use appropriate vocabulary relating to squares. In the last box the child should draw some items of their own and write the appropriate number to go with them.

Name: **Date:**

How many kites?

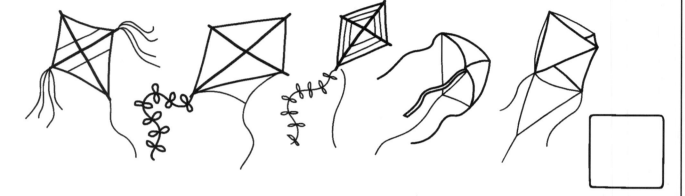

How many balloons?

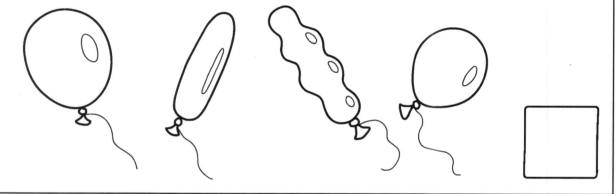

How many?

Notes for teachers

Target: Match sets of objects to numerals (Strand 1). Say and use number names; count reliably up to 10; match then compare the numbers of objects in two sets; use 'more' or 'less' to compare two numbers; recognise numerals 1 to 9 (Strand 2).

Look at each set with the child and discuss the number of items. Help the child to find the correct number to stick in the box (cut out from Resource sheet A) or to write the number in the box. If you feel that the child is confident, ask him/her whether there are more kites than balloons or fewer kites than balloons. Then discuss the fact that five is more than four and that four is less that five, In the last box the child should draw some items of their own and write the appropriate number to go with them.

Andrew Brodie: Supporting Maths © A & C Black Publishers Ltd. 2007

Name: _____ Date: _____

How many ladybirds?

How many bees?

How many?

Notes for teachers

Target: Match sets of objects to numerals (Strand 1). Say and use number names; count reliably up to 10; match then compare the numbers of objects in two sets; use 'more' or 'less' to compare two numbers; recognise numerals (Strand 2).
Look at each set with the child and discuss the number of items. Help the child to find the correct number to stick in the box (cut out from Resource sheet A) or to write the number in the box. If the child is confident, ask her/him whether there are more ladybirds than bees or fewer ladybirds than bees. Then discuss the fact that six is more than three and three is less than six. In the last box the child should draw some items of their own and write the appropriate number to go with them.

Andrew Brodie: Supporting Maths © A & C Black Publishers Ltd. 2007

How many circles?

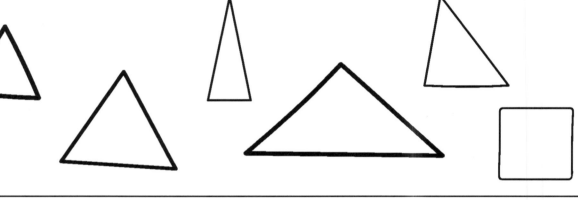

How many triangles?

How many?

Notes for teachers
Target: Match sets of objects to numerals (Strand 1). Say and use number names; count reliably up to 10; match then compare the numbers of objects in two sets; use 'more' or 'less' to compare two numbers; recognise numerals (Strand 2). Look at each set with the child and discuss the number of items. Help the child to find the correct number to stick in the box or to write the number. If the child is confident, ask him/her whether there are more circles than triangles or fewer circles than triangles. Then discuss the fact that seven is more than five and five is less than seven. In the last box the child should draw some items of their own and write the appropriate number to go with them.

Name: _____ **Date:** _____

How many parrots? ☐   How many monkeys? ☐

Notes for teachers

Target: Match sets of objects to numerals; sort objects, making choices and justifying decisions (Strand 1). Say and use number names; count reliably up to 10; match then compare the numbers of objects in two sets; use 'more' or 'less' to compare two numbers; recognise numerals (Strand 2)

Look at each picture with the child and discuss the number of items. Help the child to find the correct number to stick in the box (cut out from Resource Sheet A) or to write the number in the box. If the child is confident, ask him/her whether there are more monkeys than parrots or fewer monkeys than parrots. Unlike Worksheets 1 to 5, the child will have to answer these questions using knowledge of the number value rather than by directly comparing the pictures.

Name: _____

Date: _____

How many shells? ☐

How many fish? ☐

Notes for teachers

Target: Match sets of objects to numerals; sort objects, making choices and justifying decisions (Strand 1). Say and use number names; count reliably up to 10; match then compare the numbers of objects in two sets; use 'more' or 'less' to compare two numbers; recognise numerals (Strand 2).

Look at the picture with the child and discuss the number of items. Help the child to find the correct number to stick in the box (cut out from Resource sheet A) or to write the number in the box. If the child is confident, ask him/her whether there are more fish than shells or fewer fish than shells. Unlike Worksheets 1 to 5, the child will have to answer these questions using knowledge of the number value rather than by directly comparing the pictures.

 Andrew Brodie: Supporting Maths © A & C Black Publishers Ltd. 2007

Name: _____   **Date:** _____

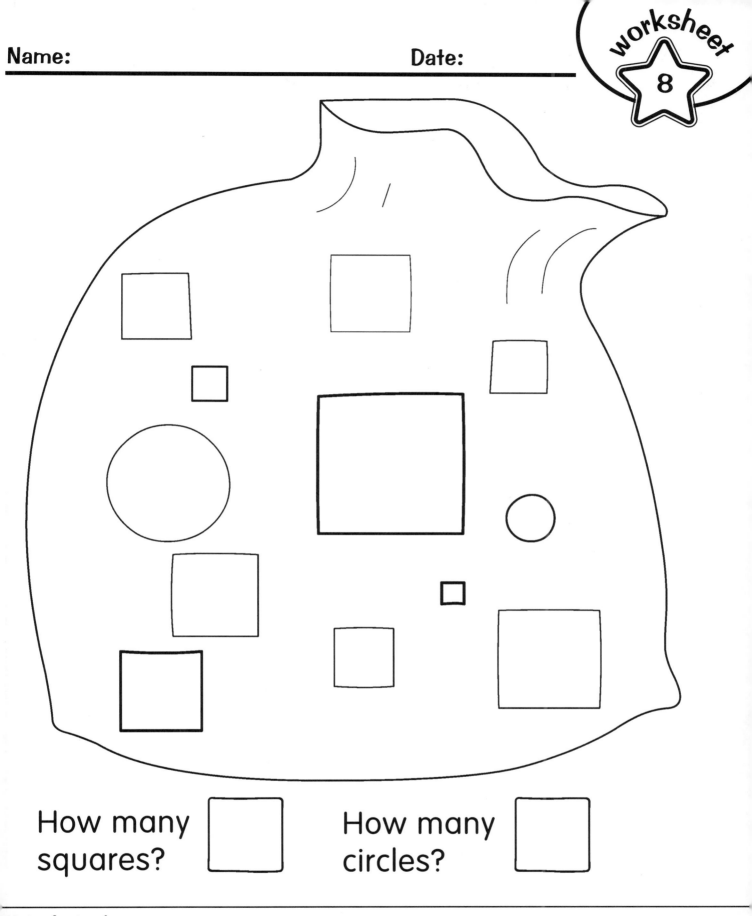

How many squares? ☐   How many circles? ☐

Notes for teachers

Target: Match sets of objects to numerals; sort objects, making choices and justifying decisions (Strand 1). Say and use number names; count reliably up to 10; match then compare the numbers of objects in two sets; use 'more' or 'less' to compare two numbers; recognise numerals (Strand 2). Use language to describe the shape and size of flat shapes (Strand 5)
Look at the picture with the child and discuss the number of items. Help the child to find the correct number to stick in the box (cut out from Resource sheet A) or to write the number in the box. If the child is confident, ask him/her whether there are more squares than circles or fewer squares than circles. With this worksheet, the difference should be obvious but the main objective of the work is the child's confidence in using the terms 'more' and 'less' in relation to the numbers two and ten. This activity also provides the opportunity to use appropriate vocabulary relating to squares and circles.

Name: _____   **Date:** _____

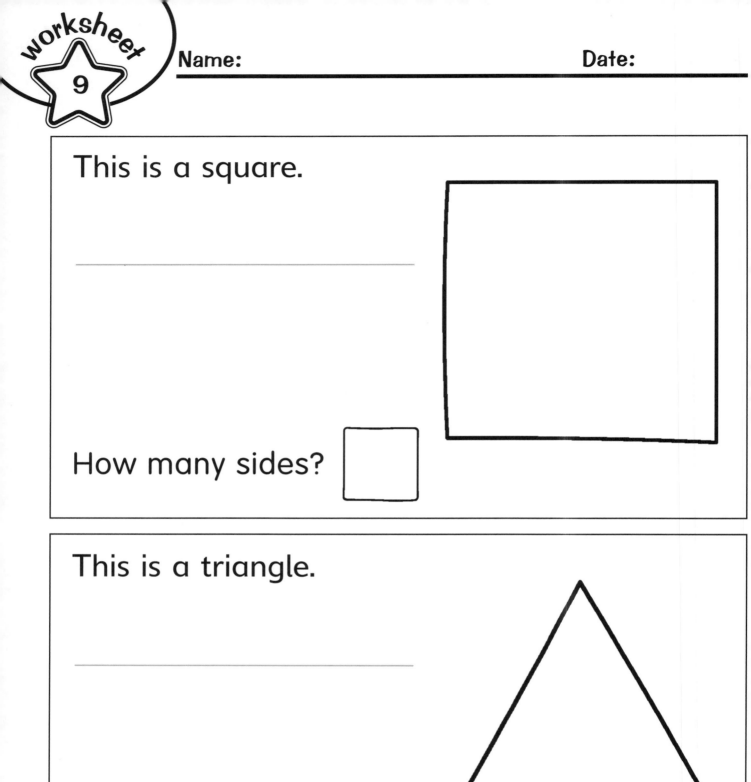

This is a square.

_____

How many sides? ☐

This is a triangle.

_____

How many sides? ☐

Notes for teachers

Target: Match sets of objects to numerals; sort objects, making choices and justifying decisions (Strand 1). Say and use number names; count reliably up to 10; match then compare the numbers of objects in two sets; use 'more' or 'less' to compare two numbers; recognise numerals (Strand 2). Use language to describe the shape and size of flat shapes (Strand 5). Look at the picture of the square with the child and discuss the number of sides. Help the child to find the correct number to stick in the box (cut out from Resource sheet A) or to write the number in the box. Use the opportunity to compare the square and the triangle and ask the child to identify differences between the two shapes.

Name:

Date:

worksheet
10

How many do you think? ☐

Now count. There are ☐ triangles.

Notes for teachers

Target: Match sets of objects to numerals (Strand 1). Say and use number names; count reliably up to 10; estimate how many objects and check by counting (Strand 2). Use language to describe the shape and size of flat shapes (Strand 5).
Ask the child how many triangles s/he thinks there are on the worksheet. Note that many children are not able to make an appropriate estimate but should be praised for making an attempt. Help him/her to write or stick the appropriate number (from Resource sheet A) in the box. Now help the child to count the number of triangles accurately. Some children find it helpful to place an object, such as a counting cube, on each item as they count it or alternatively they could place a counting cube on each item and then at the end count the number of cubes they have used. Discuss the actual number of items compared to the estimate they first made.

Andrew Brodie: Supporting Maths © A & C Black Publishers Ltd. 2007

15

Name: _____   **Date:** _____

How many do you think? ☐

Now count. There are ☐ circles.

Notes for teachers

Target: Match sets of objects to numerals (Strand 1). Say and use number names; count reliably up to 20; estimate how many objects and check by counting (Strand 2). Use language to describe the shape and size of flat shapes (Strand 5). Ask the child how many circles s/he thinks there are on the worksheet. Note that many children are not able to make an appropriate estimate but should be praised for making an attempt. Support him/her in writing or sticking the appropriate number in the box. Now help the child to count the number of circles accurately. Some children find it helpful to place an object, such as a counting cube, on each item as they count it or alternatively they could place a counting cube on each item and then at the end count the number of cubes they have used. Discuss the actual number of items compared to the estimate they first made.

Andrew Brodie: Supporting Literacy © A & C Black Publishers Ltd. 2007

How many do you think?

Now count. There are ⬜ squares.

Notes for teachers

Target: Match sets of objects to numerals (Strand 1). Say and use number names; count reliably up to 20; estimate how many objects and check by counting (Strand 2). Use language to describe the shape and size of flat shapes (Strand 5).

Ask the child how many squares s/he thinks there are on the worksheet. Note that many children are not able to make an appropriate estimate but should be praised for making an attempt. Support him/her in writing or sticking the appropriate number in the box. Now help the child to count the number of squares accurately. Some children find it helpful to place an object, such as a counting cube, on each item as they count it or alternatively they could place a counting cube on each item and then at the end count the number of cubes they have used. Discuss the actual number of items compared to the estimate they first made. You could use the opportunity to discuss the attributes of the squares i.e. each square has four sides and four corners.

Name: **Date:**

There are ☐ circles.

There are ☐ triangles.

Notes for teachers
Target: Match sets of objects to numerals (Strand 1). Say and use number names; count reliably up to 20 (Strand 2).
Use language to describe the shape and size of flat shapes (Strand 5).
Read the two sentences with the child. Help the child count the number of circles and then write the number 12 in the
space before the word circles. Ask the child how many triangles there are. Discuss the fact that there are no triangles and
that this number is represented by zero. Help the child to write the number 0 in the box before the word triangles. You
could take the opportunity to discuss the shape of the circles i.e. each circle has only one curved edge and no corners.

Name: _____   **Date:** _____

I think there are ☐ circles.

I think there are ☐ squares.

Now count.

There are ☐ circles.

There are ☐ squares.

Notes for teachers

Target: Match sets of objects to numerals; sort objects, making choices and justifying decisions (Strand 1). Say and use number names; count reliably up to 20; estimate how many objects and check by counting; compare the numbers of objects in two sets; use 'more' or 'less' to compare two numbers; recognise numerals (Strand 2). Use language to describe the shape and size of flat shapes (Strand 5).

Ask the child how many circles s/he thinks there are on the worksheet; note that many children are not able to make an appropriate estimate but should be praised for making an attempt. Support him/her in writing the appropriate number in the box. Ask the child how many squares s/he thinks there are on the worksheet. Now help the child to count the number of circles and squares accurately. Some children find it helpful to place an object, such as a counting cube, on each item as they count it or alternatively they could place a counting cube on each item and then at the end count the number of cubes they have used. Discuss the actual number of items compared to the estimate they first made. You may like to take the opportunity to compare the shapes e.g. circles have no corners whereas squares have four.

Andrew Brodie: Supporting Maths © A & C Black Publishers Ltd. 2007

Name: Date:

Write the numbers.

1 _

2 _

3 _

Now write them smaller.

1 _

2 _

3 _

Now write them even smaller.

1 _

2 _

3 _

Notes for teachers

Target: Match sets of objects to numerals (Strand 1). Say and use number names; count reliably up to 10; recognise numerals (Strand 2).
The ability to write numbers clearly and accurately is of fundamental importance. You may need to support the child in writing the numbers clearly, showing him/her where to start each number or writing the number with dotted lines for him/her to go over. Encourage the child to write each number several times.

Name: _____   **Date:** _____

worksheet
16

Write the numbers.

 4 ---------------------------------

 5 ---------------------------------

 6 ---------------------------------

Now write them smaller.

 4 ---------------------------------

 5 ---------------------------------

 6 ---------------------------------

Now write them even smaller.

 4 ---------------------------------

 5 ---------------------------------

6 ---------------------------------

Notes for teachers
Target: Match sets of objects to numerals (Strand 1). Say and use number names; count reliably up to 10; recognise numerals (Strand 2).
The ability to write numbers clearly and accurately is of fundamental importance. You may need to support the child in writing the numbers clearly, showing him/her where to start each number or writing the number with dotted lines for him/her to go over.

Name: _____   **Date:** _____

Write the numbers.

7 _ _ _ _ _ _ _ _ _ _ _ _ _ _ _ _ _ _ _

8 _ _ _ _ _ _ _ _ _ _ _ _ _ _ _ _ _ _ _

9 _ _ _ _ _ _ _ _ _ _ _ _ _ _ _ _ _ _ _

Now write them smaller.

7 _ _ _ _ _ _ _ _ _ _ _ _ _ _ _ _ _ _ _

8 _ _ _ _ _ _ _ _ _ _ _ _ _ _ _ _ _ _ _

9 _ _ _ _ _ _ _ _ _ _ _ _ _ _ _ _ _ _ _

Now write them even smaller.

7 _ _ _ _ _ _ _ _ _ _ _ _ _ _ _ _ _ _

8 _ _ _ _ _ _ _ _ _ _ _ _ _ _ _ _ _ _

9 _ _ _ _ _ _ _ _ _ _ _ _ _ _ _ _ _ _

Notes for teachers
Target: Match sets of objects to numerals (Strand 1). Say and use number names; count reliably up to 10; recognise numerals (Strand 2).
The ability to write numbers clearly and accurately is of fundamental importance. You may need to support the child in writing the numbers clearly, showing him/her where to start each number or writing the number with dotted lines for him/her to go over.

There are three triangles. Draw one more.

$3 + 1 = \boxed{}$

There are two circles. Draw one more.

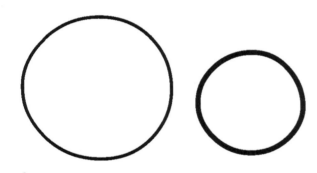

$2 + 1 = \boxed{}$

There are four squares. Draw one more.

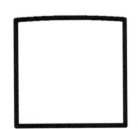

$4 + 1 = \boxed{}$

Notes for teachers

Target: Match sets of objects to numerals; talk about, recognise and recreate simple patterns (Strand 1). Say and use number names; count reliably up to 10; use 'more' or 'less' to compare two numbers; recognise numerals; use the equals sign (Strand 2). Find one more than a number between 1 and 10 (Strand 3). Begin to use the vocabulary involved in adding (Strand 4). Use language to describe the shape and size of flat shapes (Strand 5).

Adding one more is a very early stage of addition. You may find it helpful to complete several practical examples with counting equipment before asking the child to attempt this worksheet. You could, for example, with a variety of coloured counters ask the child to find three red counters, then to find one more, then ask how many s/he now has. Give plenty of praise then remind the pupil of the whole operation. 'You had three red counters. You found one more. Now you have four red counters.' On a piece of paper write: 3 + 1 = 4. Some children might find it difficult to draw the triangle, circle and square and may need shapes to draw round.

Name: _____   Date: _____

There are five circles. Draw one more.

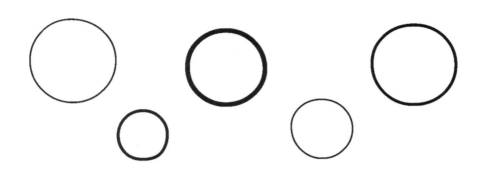

$5 + 1 = \square$

There are 6 squares. Draw one more.

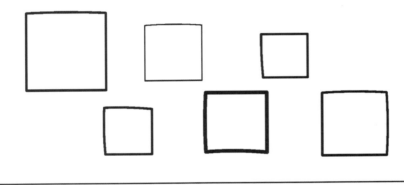

$6 + 1 = \square$

There are seven triangles. Draw one more.

$7 + 1 = \square$

Notes for teachers

Target: Match sets of objects to numerals; talk about, recognise and recreate simple patterns (Strand 1). Say and use number names; count reliably up to 10; use 'more' or 'less' to compare two numbers; recognise numerals; use the equals sign (Strand 2). Find one more than a number between 1 and 10 (Strand 3). Begin to use the vocabulary involved in adding (Strand 4). Use language to describe the shape and size of flat shapes (Strand 5).

Adding one more is a very early stage of addition. You may find it helpful to complete several practical examples with counting equipment before asking the child to attempt this worksheet. You could, for example, with a variety of coloured counters ask the child to find five green counters, then to find one more. Then ask how many s/he now has. Give plenty of praise then remind the pupil of the whole operation: 'You had five green counters. You found one more. Now you have six green counters.' On a piece of paper write: 5 + 1 = 6. Some children will experience difficulty with drawing the triangle, circle and square and may need shapes to draw round.

Name: _____   **Date:** _____

There are eight spots. Draw one more.

$8 + 1 = \boxed{}$

There are nine spots. Draw one more.

$9 + 1 = \boxed{}$

There are ten spots. Draw one more.

$10 + 1 = \boxed{}$

Notes for teachers

Target: Match sets of objects to numerals; talk about, recognise and recreate simple patterns (Strand 1). Say and use number names; count reliably up to 10; use 'more' or 'less' to compare two numbers; recognise numerals; use the equals sign (Strand 2). Find one more than a number from 1 to 10. Begin to use the vocabulary involved in adding (Strand 4). Use language to describe the shape and size of flat shapes (Strand 5).

Adding one more is a very early stage of addition. You may find it helpful to complete several practical examples with counting equipment before asking the child to attempt the worksheet. You could, for example, with a variety of coloured counters ask the child to find eight blue counters, then to find one more, then ask how many s/he now has. Give plenty of praise then remind the pupil of the whole operation: 'You had eight blue counters. You found one more. Now you have nine blue counters.' On a piece of paper write: 8 + 1 = 9.

Name: _____

Date: _____

How many circles? ☐   How many circles? ☐

How many altogether? ☐   ☐ + ☐ = ☐

How many squares? ☐   How many squares? ☐

How many altogether? ☐   ☐ + ☐ = ☐

How many triangles? ☐   How many triangles? ☐

How many altogether? ☐   ☐ + ☐ = ☐

Notes for teachers

Target: Match sets of objects to numerals; talk about, recognise and recreate simple patterns (Strand 1). Say and use number names; count reliably up to 10; recognise numerals; use the equals sign (Strand 2). Begin to relate addition to combining two groups of objects; begin to use the vocabulary involved in adding (Strand 4). Use language to describe the shape and size of flat shapes (Strand 5).

You may find it helpful to complete several practical examples with counting equipment before asking the child to attempt this worksheet. You could, for example, show the child a group of three red counters and a group of two red counters. Help the child to count the number in each group and then to count how many there are altogether. Write out clearly: 3 + 2 = 5. Discuss the written form with the child ensuring that s/he understands that this number sentence represents the practical activity of 'three and two more makes five altogether'.

How many snakes? ☐   How many snakes?

How many altogether? ☐   ☐ + ☐ = ☐

How many koalas? ☐   How many koalas? ☐

How many altogether? ☐   ☐ + ☐ = ☐

How many emus? ☐   How many emus? ☐

How many altogether? ☐   ☐ + ☐ = ☐

Notes for teachers

Target: Match sets of objects to numerals; talk about, recognise and recreate simple patterns (Strand 1). Say and use number names; count reliably up to 10; recognise numerals; use the equals sign (Strand 2). Begin to relate addition to combining two groups of objects; begin to use the vocabulary involved in adding (Strand 4).

You may find it helpful to complete several practical examples with counting equipment before asking the child to attempt this worksheet. You could, for example, show the child a group of three red counters and a group of two red counters. Help the child to count the number in each group and then to count how many there are altogether. Write out clearly: 3 + 2 = 5. Discuss the written form with the child ensuring that s/he understands that this number sentence represents the practical activity of three and two more makes five altogether.

Name: _____   **Date:** _____

Add more circles to make ten.

$7 + \boxed{} = 10$

Add more squares to make ten.

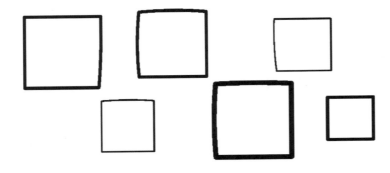

$6 + \boxed{} = 10$

Add more triangles to make ten.

$8 + \boxed{} = 10$

Notes for teachers

Target: Match sets of objects to numerals; use developing mathematical ideas and methods to solve practical problems (Strand 1). Say and use number names; count reliably up to 10; relate addition to counting on and count on in ones; use the equals sign (Strand 2). Derive and recall all pairs of numbers with a total of ten (Strand 3). Begin to relate addition to combining two groups of objects; begin to use the vocabulary involved in adding (Strand 4). Use language to describe the shape and size of flat shapes (Strand 5).

You may find it helpful to complete several practical examples with counting equipment before asking the child to attempt this worksheet. You could, for example, show the child a group of seven red counters then ask him/her to find more red counters to make ten altogether. Discuss how many more s/he had to find then show him/her the written number sentence 7 + 3 = 10 and explain it.

Andrew Brodie: Supporting Maths © A & C Black Publishers Ltd. 2007

Name: _____ **Date:** _____

Add more faces to make ten.

$$3 + \boxed{} = 10$$

Add more spots to make ten.

 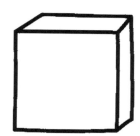

$$5 + \boxed{} = 10$$

Add more apples to make ten.

$$7 + \boxed{} = 10$$

Notes for teachers

Target: Match sets of objects to numerals; use developing mathematical ideas and methods to solve practical problems (Strand 1). Say and use number names; count reliably up to 10; relate addition to counting on and count on in ones; use the equals sign (Strand 2). Derive and recall all pairs of numbers with a total of ten (Strand 3). Begin to relate addition to combining two groups of objects; begin to use the vocabulary involved in adding (Strand 4). Use language to describe the shape and size of flat shapes (Strand 5).

You may find it helpful to complete several practical examples with counting equipment before asking the child to attempt this worksheet. You could, for example, show the child a group of four blue counters then ask him/her to find more blue counters to make ten altogether. Discuss how many more s/he had to find then show him/her the written number sentence 4 + 6 = 10 and discuss this to ensure s/he understands.

Name:

Date:

Continue the patterns.

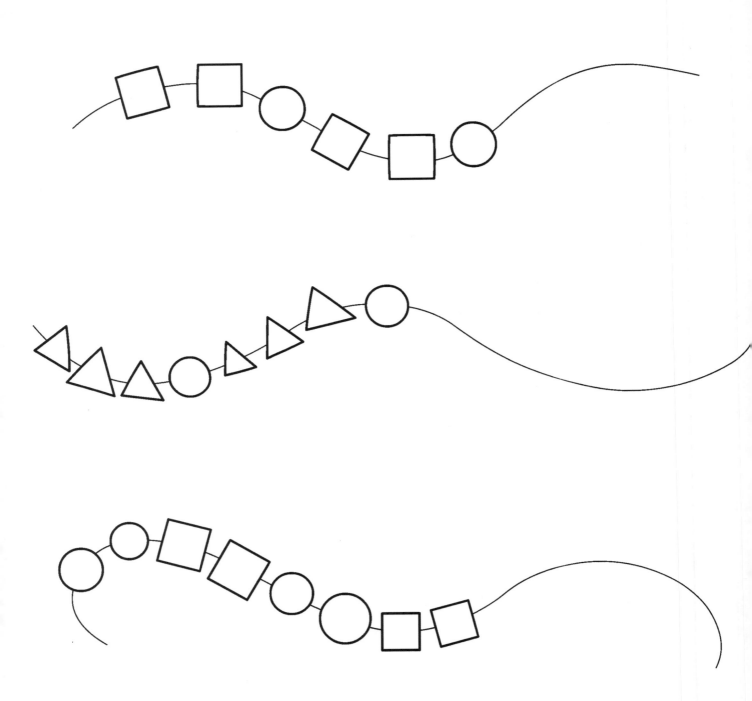

Notes for teachers

Target: Use developing mathematical ideas and methods to solve practical problems; talk about, recognise and recreate simple patterns (Strand 1). Say and use number names in order in familiar contexts (Strand 2). Count repeated groups of the same size (Strand 4). Use language to describe the shape and size of flat shapes (Strand 5). Talk about, recognise and recreate simple patterns; sort familiar objects and count how many objects share a particular property, presenting results using pictures, drawings or numerals (Strand 7).

You may find it helpful to complete several practical examples by creating patterns with counters, model shapes or beads then asking the child to continue the pattern that you have made.

Andrew Brodie: Supporting Maths © A & C Black Publishers Ltd. 2007

3 + 2 = ☐

5 + 4 = ☐

7 + 1 = ☐

8 + 3 = ☐

6 + 2 = ☐

4 + 3 = ☐

5 + 1 = ☐

1 + 1 = ☐

Notes for teachers

Target: Match sets of objects to numerals (Strand 1). Say and use number names; count reliably up to 10; recognise numerals; use the equals sign (Strand 2). Derive and recall addition facts for totals to at least 5 (Strand 3). Begin to relate addition to combining two groups of objects; begin to use the vocabulary involved in adding (Strand 4).

You may find it helpful to complete several practical examples with counting equipment before asking the child to attempt this worksheet. You could, for example, show the child a group of three red counters and a group of two red counters. Help the child to count the number in each group and then to count how many there are altogether. Write out clearly: 3 + 2 = 5. Discuss the written form with the child ensuring that s/he understands that this number sentence represents the practical activity of 'three and two more makes five altogether'.

Andrew Brodie: Supporting Maths © A & C Black Publishers Ltd. 2007

Name: _____

Date: _____

$3 + 6 = \boxed{}$

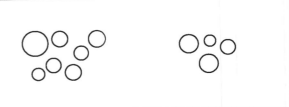

$7 + 4 = \boxed{}$

$8 + 2 = \boxed{}$

$9 + 1 = \boxed{}$

$7 + 3 = \boxed{}$

$6 + 4 = \boxed{}$

$5 + 5 = \boxed{}$

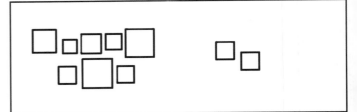

$10 + 0 = \boxed{}$

Notes for teachers

Target: Match sets of objects to numerals (Strand 1). Say and use number names; count reliably up to 10; recognise numerals; use the equals sign (Strand 2). Derive and recall all pairs of numbers with a total of 10 and addition facts for totals to at least 5 (Strand 3). Begin to relate addition to combining two groups of objects; begin to use the vocabulary involved in adding (Strand 4).

You may find it helpful to complete several practical examples with counting equipment before asking the child to attempt this worksheet. You could, for example, show the child a group of three red counters and a group of six red counters. Help the child to count the number in each group and then to count how many there are altogether. Write out clearly: 3 + 6 = 9. Discuss the written form with the child ensuring that s/he understands that this number sentence represents the practical activity of 'three and six more makes nine altogether'.

Name: _____   **Date:** _____

$$5 + 6 = \boxed{}$$

$$7 + 7 = \boxed{}$$

$$7 + 5 = \boxed{}$$

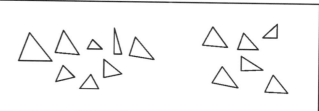

$$8 + 6 = \boxed{}$$

$$9 + 4 = \boxed{}$$

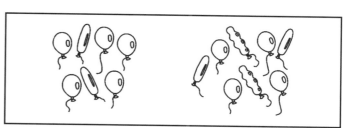

$$7 + 8 = \boxed{}$$

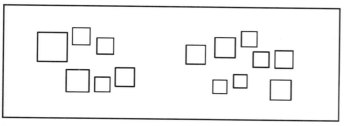

$$6 + 8 = \boxed{}$$

$$10 + 5 = \boxed{}$$

Notes for teachers:
Target: Match sets of objects to numerals (Strand 1). Say and use number names; count reliably up to 10; recognise numerals; use the equals sign (Strand 2). Derive and recall all pairs of numbers with a total of 10 and addition facts for totals to at least 5; recall the doubles of all numbers to at least 10 (Strand 3). Begin to relate addition to combining two groups of objects; begin to use the vocabulary involved in adding (Strand 4).
You may find it helpful to complete several practical examples with counting equipment before asking the child to attempt the worksheet.

Name: _____   **Date:** _____

8 + 4 = ☐

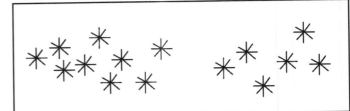

9 + 6 = ☐

6 + 7 = ☐

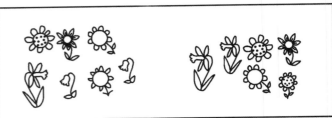

7 + 6 = ☐

7 + 4 = ☐

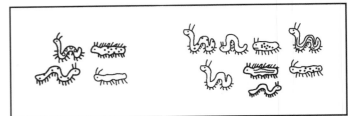

4 + 8 = ☐

6 + 9 = ☐

4 + 7 = ☐

Notes for teachers

Target: Match sets of objects to numerals (Strand 1). Say and use number names; count reliably up to 10; recognise numerals; use the equals sign (Strand 2). Derive and recall all pairs of numbers with a total of 10 and addition facts for totals to at least 5 (Strand 3). Begin to relate addition to combining two groups of objects; begin to use the vocabulary involved in adding (Strand 4).

You may find it helpful to complete several practical examples with counting equipment before asking the child to attempt this worksheet.

Name: _____ Date: _____

1 + 1 =

6 + 6 =

3 + 3 =

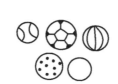 

5 + 5 =

7 + 7 =

2 + 2 =

4 + 4 =

8 + 8 =

Notes for teachers
Target: Match sets of objects to numerals (Strand 1). Say and use number names; count reliably up to 10; recognise numerals; use the equals sign (Strand 2). Derive and recall all pairs of numbers with a total of 10 and addition facts for totals to at least 5; recall the doubles of all numbers to at least 10 (Strand 3). Begin to relate addition to combining two groups of objects; begin to use the vocabulary involved in adding (Strand 4).
You may find it helpful to complete several practical examples with counting equipment before asking the child to attempt this worksheet.

Name: _____   **Date:** _____

$3 - 2 =$ ☐

$6 - 4 =$ ☐

$7 - 5 =$ ☐

$5 - 1 =$ ☐

$4 - 2 =$ ☐

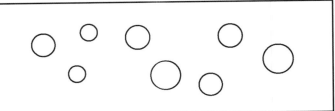

$8 - 4 =$ ☐

$9 - 6 =$ ☐

$7 - 1 =$ ☐

Notes for teachers

Target: Use developing mathematical ideas and methods to solve practical problems; match sets of objects to numerals (Strand 1). Say and use number names; count reliably up to 10; recognise numerals; use the equals sign (Strand 2). Derive and recall all pairs of numbers with a total of 10 and addition facts for totals to at least 5; work out the corresponding subtraction facts (Strand 3). Begin to relate subtraction to 'taking away'; begin to use the vocabulary involved in subtracting (Strand 4).

You may find it helpful to complete several practical examples with counting equipment before asking the child to attempt this worksheet. Note that this activity is concerned with 'taking away' rather than 'finding the difference' so, for example, in the first question you could use two small pieces of paper to cover two of the koalas so that they have effectively been 'taken away'.

Andrew Brodie: Supporting Maths © A & C Black Publishers Ltd. 2007

Name: _____   **Date:** _____

$$5 - 2 = \square$$

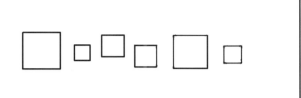

$$6 - 1 = \square$$

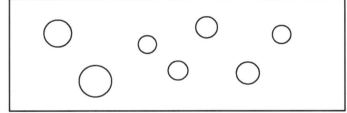

$$7 - 3 = \square$$

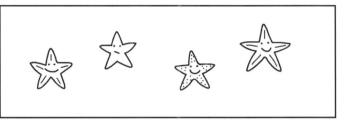

$$4 - 2 = \square$$

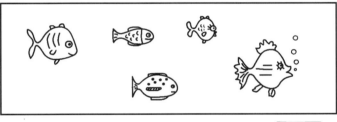

$$5 - 4 = \square$$

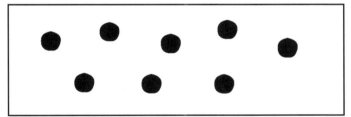

$$8 - 5 = \square$$

$$6 - 6 = \square$$

$$9 - 1 = \square$$

Notes for teachers

Target: Use developing mathematical ideas and methods to solve practical problems; match sets of objects to numerals (Strand 1). Say and use number names; count reliably up to 10; recognise numerals; use the equals sign (Strand 2). Derive and recall all pairs of numbers with a total of 10 and addition facts for totals to at least 5; work out the corresponding subtraction facts (Strand 3). Begin to relate subtraction to 'taking away'; begin to use the vocabulary involved in subtracting (Strand 4).

You may find it helpful to complete several practical examples with counting equipment before asking the child to attempt this worksheet. Note that this activity is concerned with 'taking away' rather than 'finding the difference' so, for example, in the first question you could use two small pieces of paper to cover two ducks so that they have effectively been taken away. Note that the question 6 – 6 may need extra discussion as many children find the concept of zero quite difficult.

Name: **Date:**

$3 + 2 =$ ☐

$6 + 4 =$ ☐

$7 + 2 =$ ☐

$5 + 1 =$ ☐

$4 + 2 =$ ☐

$2 + 6 =$ ☐

Notes for teachers

Target: Use developing mathematical ideas and methods to solve practical problems; solve problems involving counting, adding; answer a question by selecting and using suitable equipment (Strand 1). Say and use number names; count reliably up to 10; recognise numerals; use the equals sign (Strand 2). Derive and recall all pairs of numbers with a total of 10 and addition facts for totals to at least 5; work out the corresponding subtraction facts (Strand 3). Add mentally a one-digit number to a one-digit number (Strand 4).

The ladder makes a useful number line where the child can see that the number goes up when we add and goes down when we subtract. Discuss each question with the child e.g. for the first question, ask the child to start on rung number 3 then to go up 2. S/he should see that this reaches number 5.

Name: _____   **Date:** _____

$5 + 2 = \square$

$3 + 4 = \square$

$8 + 2 = \square$

$5 + 4 = \square$

$6 + 2 = \square$

$2 + 2 = \square$

Notes for teachers

Target: Use developing mathematical ideas and methods to solve practical problems; solve problems involving counting, adding; answer a question by selecting and using suitable equipment (Strand 1). Say and use number names; count reliably up to 10; recognise numerals; use the equals sign (Strand 2). Derive and recall all pairs of numbers with a total of 10 and addition facts for totals to at least 5; work out the corresponding subtraction facts (Strand 3). Add mentally a one-digit number to a one-digit number (Strand 4).

The ladder makes a useful number line where the child can see that the number goes up when we add and goes down when we subtract. Discuss each question with the child e.g. for the first question, ask the child to start on rung number 5 then to go up 2. S/he should see that this reaches number 7.

Name: _____

Date: _____

5 + 5 = ☐   3 + 1 = ☐   0 + 2 = ☐

3 + 4 = ☐   8 + 2 = ☐   3 + 3 = ☐

Notes for teachers

Target: Use developing mathematical ideas and methods to solve practical problems; solve problems involving counting, adding; answer a question by selecting and using suitable equipment (Strand 1). Say and use number names; count reliably up to 10; recognise numerals; use the equals sign (Strand 2). Derive and recall all pairs of numbers with a total of 10 and addition facts for totals to at least 5; work out the corresponding subtraction facts (Strand 3). Add mentally a one-digit number to a one-digit number (Strand 4).

The ladder makes a useful number line where the child can see that the number goes up when we add and goes down when we subtract. Discuss each question with the child e.g. for the first question, ask the child to start on rung number 5 then to go up 5. S/he should see that this reaches number 10.

Name: _____ **Date:** _____

$5 + 1 =$ ☐

$3 + 1 =$ ☐

$1 + 1 =$ ☐

$7 + 1 =$ ☐

$8 + 1 =$ ☐

$0 + 1 =$ ☐

Notes for teachers

Target: Use developing mathematical ideas and methods to solve practical problems; solve problems involving counting, adding; answer a question by selecting and using suitable equipment (Strand 1). Say and use number names; count reliably up to 10; recognise numerals; use the equals sign (Strand 2). Find one more or one less than a number from 1 to 10 (Strand 3). Add mentally a one-digit number to a one-digit number (Strand 4).

The ladder makes a useful number line where the child can see that the number goes up when we add and goes down when we subtract. Discuss each question with the child: e.g. for the first question, ask the child to start on rung number 5 then to go up 1. S/he should see that this reaches number 6.

Name: **Date:**

6 + 1 = ☐

9 + 1 = ☐

4 + 1 = ☐

0 + 1 = ☐

9 + 1 = ☐

8 + 1 = ☐

Notes for teachers

Target: Use developing mathematical ideas and methods to solve practical problems; solve problems involving counting, adding; answer a question by selecting and using suitable equipment (Strand 1). Say and use number names; count reliably up to 10; recognise numerals; use the equals sign (Strand 2). Find one more or one less than a number from 1 to 10 (Strand 3). Add mentally a one-digit number to a one-digit number (Strand 4).

The ladder makes a useful number line where the child can see that the number goes up when we add and goes down when we subtract. Discuss each question with the child e.g. for the first question, ask the child to start on rung number 6 then to go up 1. S/he should see that this reaches number 7.

Name:

Date:

9 + 2 = ☐   8 + 4 = ☐   7 + 5 = ☐

5 + 8 = ☐   4 + 9 = ☐   9 + 6 = ☐

Notes for teachers

Target: Use developing mathematical ideas and methods to solve practical problems; solve problems involving counting, adding; answer a question by selecting and using suitable equipment (Strand 1). Read and write numerals, numbers from 0 to at least 20; recognise numerals; use the equals sign (Strand 2). Derive and recall all pairs of numbers with a total of 10 and addition facts for totals to at least 5; work out the corresponding subtraction facts (Strand 3). Add mentally a one-digit number to a one-digit number (Strand 4).

The ladder makes a useful number line where the child can see that the number goes up when we add and goes down when we subtract. Discuss each question with the child e.g. for the first question, ask the child to start on rung number 9 then to go up 2. S/he should see that this reaches number 11.

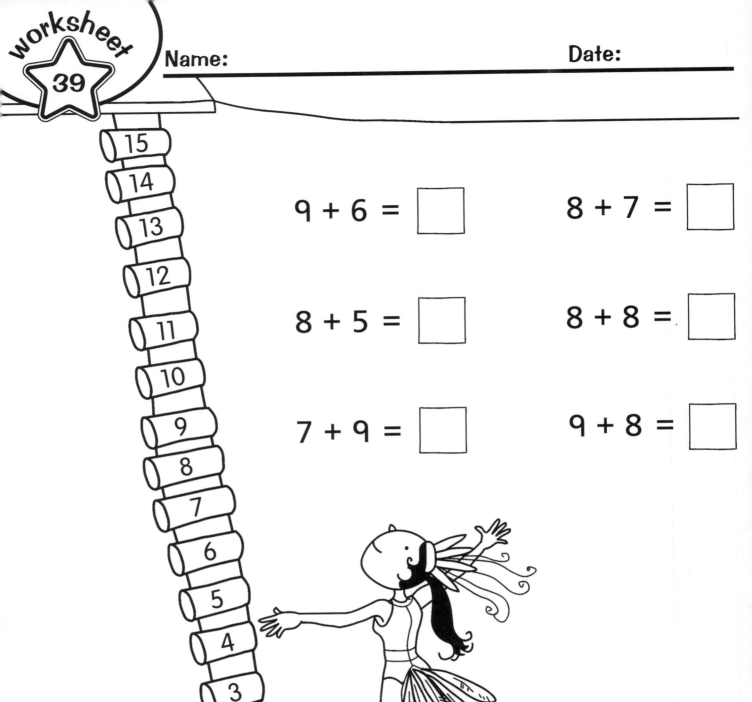

$9 + 6 =$ ☐

$8 + 7 =$ ☐

$8 + 5 =$ ☐

$8 + 8 =$ ☐

$7 + 9 =$ ☐

$9 + 8 =$ ☐

Notes for teachers

Target: Use developing mathematical ideas and methods to solve practical problems; solve problems involving counting, adding; answer a question by selecting and using suitable equipment (Strand 1). Read and write numerals, numbers from 0 to at least 20; recognise numerals; use the equals sign (Strand 2). Derive and recall all pairs of numbers with a total of 10 and addition facts for totals to at least 5; work out the corresponding subtraction facts (Strand 3). Add mentally a one-digit number to a one-digit number (Strand 4).

The ladder makes a useful number line where the child can see that the number goes up when we add and goes down when we subtract. Discuss each question with the child e.g. for the first question, ask the child to start on rung number 9 then to go up 6. S/he should see that this reaches number 15.

Name: _____

Date: _____

$6 - 2 = \square$ $9 - 5 = \square$ $4 - 3 = \square$

$8 - 2 = \square$ $7 - 6 = \square$ $5 - 2 = \square$

Notes for teachers:
Target: Use developing mathematical ideas and methods to solve practical problems; solve problems involving counting, subtracting; answer a question by selecting and using suitable equipment (Strand 1). Say and use number names; count reliably up to 10; recognise numerals; use the equals sign (Strand 2). Secure knowledge of subtraction facts (Strand 3). Subtract one-digit numbers from one-digit and two-digit numbers (Strand 4).
The ladder makes a useful number line where the child can see that the number goes up when we add and goes down when we subtract. Discuss each question with the child e.g. for the first question, ask the child to start on rung number 6 then to go down 2. S/he should see that this reaches number 4.

Name: _____   **Date:** _____

$8 - 2 =$ ☐

$9 - 7 =$ ☐

$8 - 3 =$ ☐

$10 - 2 =$ ☐

$7 - 4 =$ ☐

$5 - 4 =$ ☐

Notes for teachers

Target: Use developing mathematical ideas and methods to solve practical problems; solve problems involving counting, subtracting; answer a question by selecting and using suitable equipment (Strand 1). Say and use number names; count reliably up to 10; recognise numerals; use the equals sign (Strand 2). Secure knowledge of subtraction facts (Strand 3). Subtract one-digit numbers from one-digit and two-digit numbers (Strand 4).
The ladder makes a useful number line where the child can see that the number goes up when we add and goes down when we subtract. Discuss each question with the child e.g. for the first question, ask the child to start on rung number 8 then to go down 2. S/he should see that this reaches number 6.

$7 - 3 =$ ☐ $9 - 2 =$ ☐ $8 - 5 =$ ☐

$10 - 6 =$ ☐ $6 - 4 =$ ☐ $5 - 5 =$ ☐

Notes for teachers

Target: Use developing mathematical ideas and methods to solve practical problems; solve problems involving counting, subtracting; answer a question by selecting and using suitable equipment (Strand 1). Say and use number names; count reliably up to 10; recognise numerals; use the equals sign (Strand 2). Secure knowledge of subtraction facts (Strand 3). Subtract one-digit numbers from one-digit and two-digit numbers (Strand 4).

The ladder makes a useful number line where the child can see that the number goes up when we add and goes down when we subtract. Discuss each question with the child e.g. for the first question, ask the child to start on rung number 7 then to go down 3. S/he should see that this reaches number 4.

$$7 - 1 = \boxed{} \qquad 9 - 1 = \boxed{} \qquad 4 - 1 = \boxed{}$$

$$10 - 1 = \boxed{} \qquad 8 - 1 = \boxed{} \qquad 3 - 1 = \boxed{}$$

Notes for teachers

Target: Use developing mathematical ideas and methods to solve practical problems; solve problems involving counting, subtracting; answer a question by selecting and using suitable equipment (Strand 1). Say and use number names; count reliably up to 10; recognise numerals; use the equals sign (Strand 2). Find one more or one less than a number from 1 to 10; secure knowledge of subtraction facts (Strand 3). Subtract one-digit numbers from one-digit and two-digit numbers (Strand 4).

The ladder makes a useful number line where the child can see that the number goes up when we add and goes down when we subtract. Discuss each question with the child e.g. for the first question, ask the child to start on rung number 7 then to go down 1. S/he should see that this reaches number 6.

$9 - 6 =$ ☐

$12 - 7 =$ ☐

$14 - 8 =$ ☐

$15 - 6 =$ ☐

$11 - 3 =$ ☐

$13 - 4 =$ ☐

Notes for teachers

Target: Use developing mathematical ideas and methods to solve practical problems; solve problems involving counting, subtracting; answer a question by selecting and using suitable equipment (Strand 1). Read and write numerals from 0 to at least 20; recognise numerals; use the equals sign (Strand 2). Secure knowledge of subtraction facts (Strand 3). Subtract one-digit numbers from one-digit and two-digit numbers (Strand 4).

The ladder makes a useful number line where the child can see that the number goes up when we add and goes down when we subtract. Discuss each question with the child e.g. for the first question, ask the child to start on rung number 9 then to go down 6. S/he should see that this reaches number 3.

Name: _____ Date: _____

10 − 6 = ☐

12 − 3 = ☐

15 − 9 = ☐

11 − 5 = ☐

13 − 3 = ☐

14 − 4 = ☐

Notes for teachers

Target: Use developing mathematical ideas and methods to solve practical problems; solve problems involving counting, subtracting; answer a question by selecting and using suitable equipment (Strand 1). Read and write numerals, numbers from 0 to at least 20; recognise numerals; use the equals sign (Strand 2). Secure knowledge of subtraction facts (Strand 3). Subtract one-digit numbers from one-digit and two-digit numbers (Strand 4).

The ladder makes a useful number line where the child can see that the number goes up when we add and goes down when we subtract. Discuss each question with the child e.g. for the first question, ask the child to start on rung number 10 then to go down 6. S/he should see that this reaches number 4. You may need to provide extra help on the question 15 − 9 as it is very easy for a child to lose count when going down so many rungs. The final two questions are useful in demonstrating subtractions that result in 10.

Name: _____ **Date:** _____

A clock face

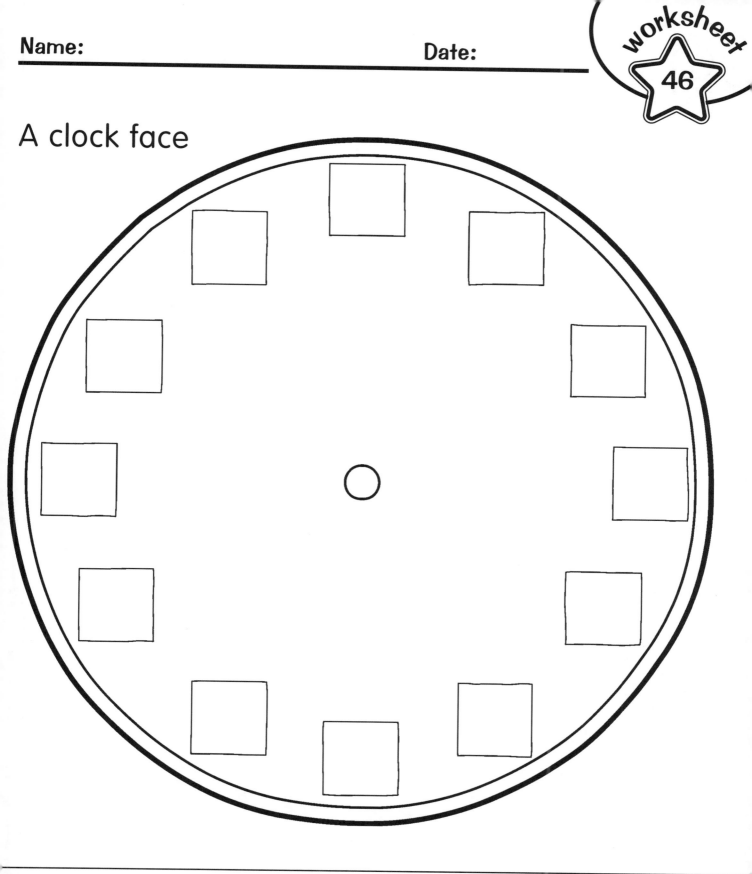

Notes for teachers

Target: Talk about, recognise and recreate simple patterns (Strand 1). Say and use number names; count aloud in ones, twos; read and write numerals and position these numbers on a number track and number line; order numbers, using the related vocabulary; say the number that is one more or less than a given number (Strand 2). Find one more or one less than a number from 1 to 10 (Strand 3). Use everyday words to describe position (Strand 5). Use everyday language related to time; order and sequence familiar events (Strand 6). Talk about, recognise and recreate simple patterns (Strand 7).
The clock face is a very useful resource in early number work as it provides a familiar number track. Discuss the classroom clock with the child, encouraging him/her to notice the position of the numbers. Support him/her in writing or sticking the numbers in the correct places. (Numbers of the correct size for this activity can be found on Resource sheet G). Take the opportunity to count around the face, 1, 2, etc, pointing out that the clock is not like most number lines because it does not show zero and it only goes as far as 12 then starts again.

Number cards

0	1	2	3	4	5
6	7	8	0	1	2
3	4	5	6	7	8
0	1	2	3	4	5
6	7	8	0	1	2
3	4	5	6	7	8

Notes for teachers

Target: Say and use the number names in order; recognise numerals 1 to 9; numbers from 0; count reliably up to 10 (Strand 2).

These number cards provide an excellent resource to be used in conjunction with Resource sheet C, where the numbers are written in words, and Resource sheets E or H, which feature simple dot patterns for counting. You could photocopy all of these resource sheets so that you can ask the child to match the sets of cards e.g. the child could match the card of five random dots from Resource sheet E with the 5 card from this sheet or with both the 5 card from this sheet and the five word card from Resource sheet C.

Andrew Brodie: Supporting Maths © A & C Black Publishers Ltd. 2007

Resource sheet B

Number cards

9	10	11	12	13	14
15	16	17	9	10	11
12	13	14	15	16	17
9	10	11	12	13	14
15	16	17	9	10	11
12	13	14	15	16	17

Notes for teachers

Target: Say and use the number names in order; count reliably at least 20 objects; read and write numerals, numbers from 0 to at least 20 (Strand 2).

These number cards provide an excellent resource to be used in conjunction with Resource sheets C and D, where the numbers are written in words, and Resource sheets F or G, which feature simple dot patterns for counting. You may like to photocopy all of these resource sheets so that you can ask the child to match the sets of cards e.g. the child could match the card of fifteen random dots from Resource sheet F with the 15 number card from this sheet or with both the 15 card from this sheet and the fifteen word card from Resource sheet D.

Number and word cards

18	19	20	18	19	20
18	19	20	18	19	20

zero	one	two
three	four	five
six	seven	eight
nine	ten	

Notes for teachers

Target: Say and use the number names in order; recognise numerals 1 to 9; numbers from 0; count reliably up to 10 (Strand 2)
These number cards provide an excellent resource to be used in conjunction with Resource sheet C, where the numbers are written in words, and Resource sheets E or H, which feature simple dot patterns for counting. You could photocopy all of these resource sheets so that you can ask the child to match the sets of cards e.g. the child could match the card of five random dots from Resource sheet E with the 5 card from this sheet or with both the 5 card from this sheet and the five word card from Resource sheet C.

 Andrew Brodie: Supporting Maths © A & C Black Publishers Ltd. 2007

Word cards

eleven	twelve
eleven	twelve
thirteen	fourteen
fifteen	sixteen
seventeen	eighteen

Notes for teachers
Target: Say and use the number names in order; count reliably at least 20 objects; read and write numerals, numbers from 0 to at least 20 (Strand 2).
The word cards on this sheet are to be used with the number cards from Resource sheets B and C and the counting cards from Resource sheets F and G.

Counting cards

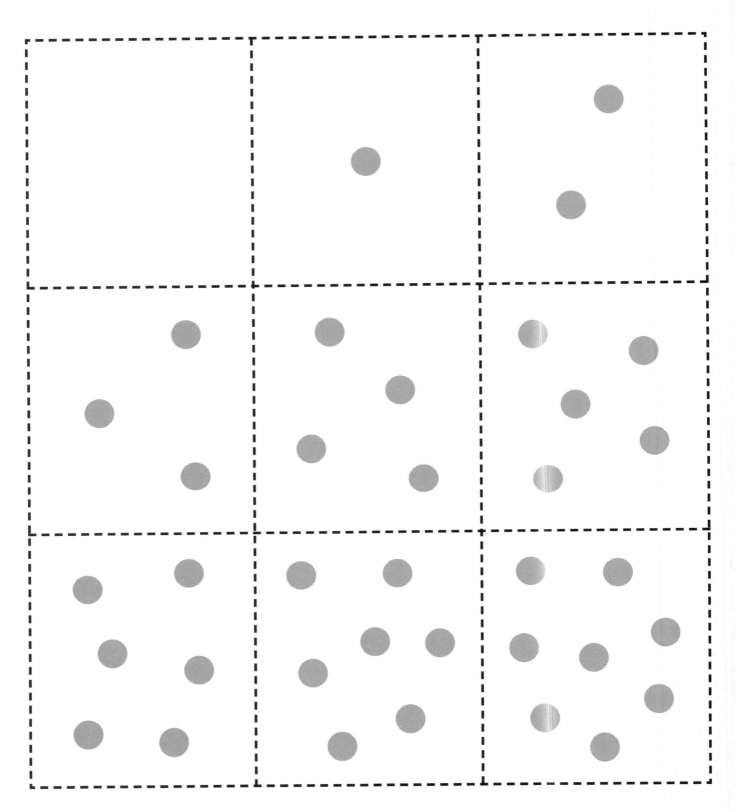

Notes for teachers
Target: Say and use the number names in order; recognise numerals 1 to 9; numbers from 0; count reliably up to 10 (Strand 2)
These counting cards are to be used in conjunction with the number cards from Resource sheet A and the word cards from Resource sheet C.

Resource sheet F

Counting cards

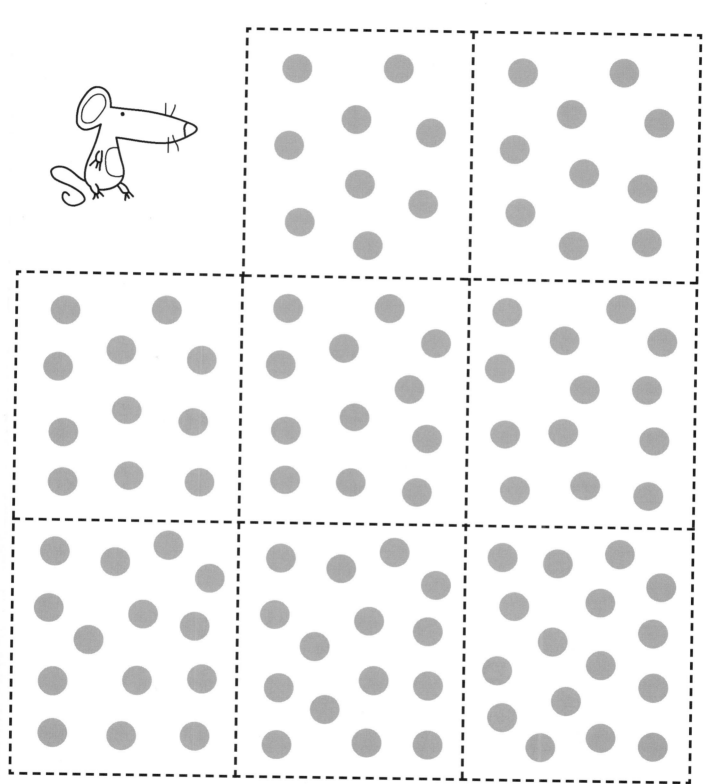

Counting cards

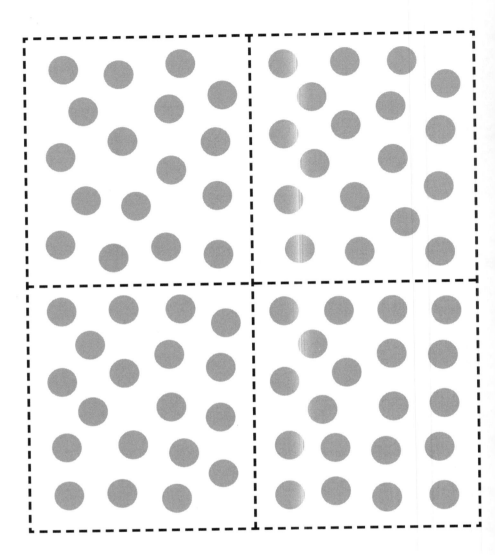

1	2	3	4	5	6
7	8	9	10	11	12

Notes for teachers

Target: Say and use the number names in order; recognise numerals 1 to 9; numbers from 0; count reliably up to 10 (Strand 2). These counting cards are to be used in conjunction with the number cards on Resource sheets B and C and the word cards from Resource sheet D.

Resource sheet H

Dice patterns and shapes

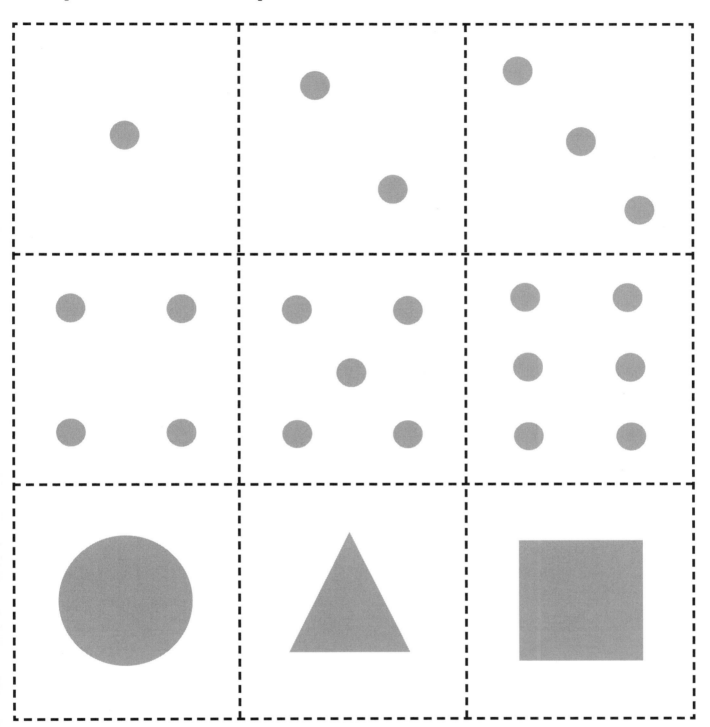

Notes for teachers

Target: Say and use the number names in order; recognise numerals 1 to 9; numbers from 0; count reliably up to 10 (Strand 2). Use language to describe the shape and size of flat shapes; visualise and name common 2-D shapes and describe their features (Strand 5).

The spots on these counting cards are presented in the same pattern as on dice or dominoes. These spot patterns will become familiar to the child and will become easy to recognise when s/he is participating in maths class games. These spot cards are to be used in conjunction with the number cards on Resource sheet A and the word cards from Resource sheet C. The final three cards show the shapes circle, triangle and square. The cards can be used as flashcards to ask the child to identify the shapes and also as a focus for discussion and comparison e.g. the child could state that the square has four sides, the triangle has three sides and the circle has one curved edge. S/he could state that the square has four corners, the triangle has three corners and the circle has no corners.

Shapes

Name: _____

This is my circle.

Notes for teachers

Target: Use language such as 'circle' or 'bigger' to describe the shape and size of flat shapes; visualise and name common 2-D shapes and describe their features (Strand 5).

Photocopy this sheet and then ask the child to cut out the circle as carefully and accurately as possible. Ask the child to copy the sentence 'This is my circle'. Discuss the shape with the child.

Resource sheet J

Shapes

Name: _____

This is my square.

Notes for teachers

Target: Use language such as 'circle' or 'bigger' to describe the shape and size of flat shapes; visualise and name common 2-D shapes and describe their features (Strand 5).

Photocopy this sheet and then ask the child to cut out the square as carefully and accurately as possible. Ask the child to copy the sentence 'This is my square'. Discuss the shape with the child.

Andrew Brodie: Supporting Maths © A & C Black Publishers Ltd. 2007

Shapes

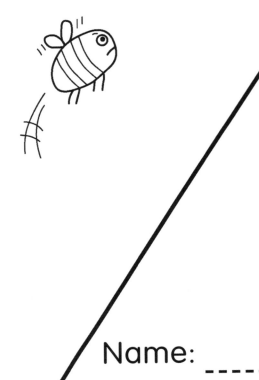

Name: _

This is my triangle.

Notes for teachers
Target: Use language such as 'circle' or 'bigger' to describe the shape and size of flat shapes; visualise and name common 2-D shapes and describe their features (Strand 5).
Photocopy this sheet and then ask the child to cut out the triangle as carefully and accurately as possible. Ask the child to copy the sentence 'This is my triangle'. Discuss the shape with the child.

Resource sheet L

Clock numbers

Notes for teachers

Target: Describe simple patterns and relationships involving numbers (Strand 1). Read and write numerals from 0 to 12; say the number that is 1 more or less than any given number (Strand 2). Count on or back in ones (Strand 3). Use vocabulary related to time; read the time to the hour and half hour (Strand 6).

Apart from using the clock face to practise telling the time, it can also be used as a number line. The child can gain confidence in recognising the relative positions of the numbers but will need to be shown that the clock face is different from a normal number line in that it cannot show numbers before 1 or after 12.

Number ladders

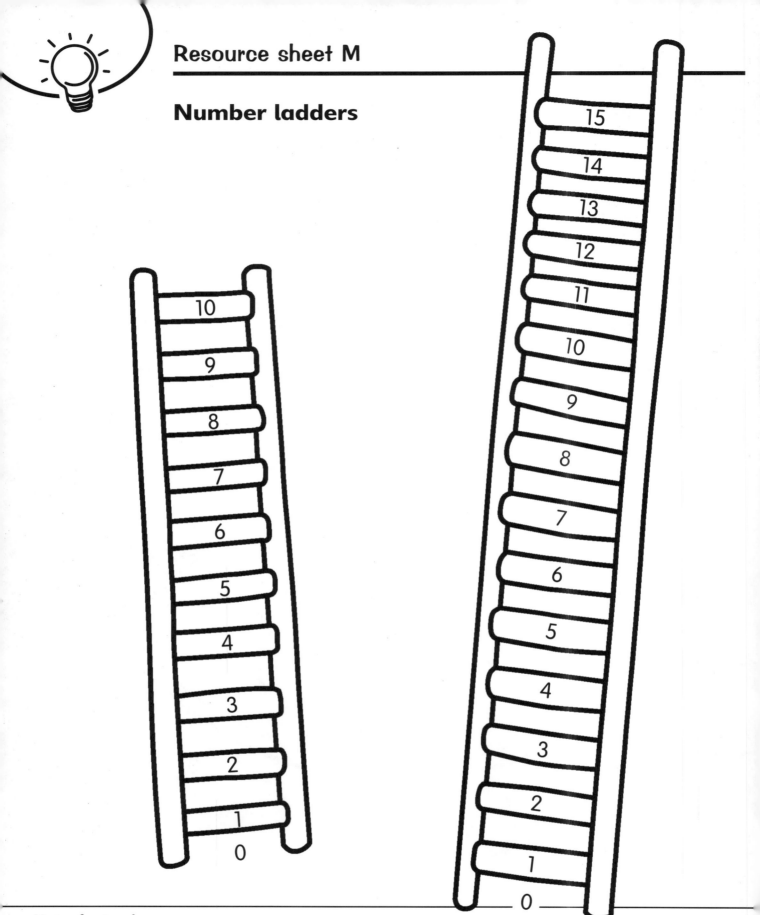

Notes for teachers

Target: Use developing mathematical ideas and methods to solve practical problems; solve problems involving counting, adding; answer a question by selecting and using suitable equipment (Strand 1). Say and use number names; count reliably at least 20 objects; recognise numerals; use the equals sign (Strand 2). Find one more or one less than a number from 1 to 10 (Strand 3). Add mentally a one-digit number to a one-digit or two-digit number; subtract one-digit numbers from one-digit and two-digit numbers (Strand 4).

The ladder makes a useful number line where the child can see that the number goes up when we add and goes down when we subtract. This resource sheet can be used whenever a child has to add or subtract numbers in the range 0 to 15.